Table of Contents

Y0-CBP-593

Table of Contents (continued)

Chapter 2

Table of Contents (continued)

Chapter 3

Table of Contents (continued)

Chapter 4

Safety Guidelines for Science Investigations

1. **Follow instructions.** Listen carefully to your teacher's instructions. Ask questions if you don't know what to do.

2. **Don't taste things.** No tasting anything or putting it near your mouth unless your teacher says it is safe to do so.

3. **Smell substances like a chemist.** When you smell a substance, don't put your nose near it. Instead, gently move the air from above the substance to your nose. This is how chemists smell substances.

4. **Protect your eyes.** Wear safety goggles if something wet could splash into your eyes, if powder or dust might get in your eyes, or if something sharp could fly into your eyes.

5. **Protect your hands.** Wear gloves if you are working with materials or chemicals that could irritate your skin.

6. **Keep your hands away from your face.** Do not touch your face, mouth, ears, eyes, or nose while working with chemicals, plants, or animals.

7. **Tell your teacher if you have allergies.** This will keep you safe and comfortable during science class.

8. **Be calm and careful.** Move carefully and slowly around the classroom. Save your outdoor behavior for recess.

9. **Report all spills, accidents, and injuries to your teacher.** Tell your teacher if something spills, if there is an accident, or if someone gets injured.

10. **Avoid anything that could cause a burn.** Allow your teacher to work with hot water or hot equipment.

11. **Wash your hands after class.** Make sure to wash your hands thoroughly with soap and water after handling plants, animals, or science materials.

© 2018 The Regents of the University of California. All rights reserved. Permission granted to photocopy for classroom use.

What Is a Scientific Explanation?

1. It answers a question about how or why something happens.

2. It is based on the ideas you have learned from investigations and text.

3. It uses scientific language.

4. It is written for an audience.

5. It describes things that are not easy to observe.

© 2018 The Regents of the University of California. All rights reserved. Permission granted to photocopy for classroom use.

Name: _____ Date: _____

Handbook of Traits **Scavenger Hunt**

Directions:

1. Refer to *Handbook of Traits* to help you to complete the scavenger hunt below.

2. In each box, write about one organism.

an organism that builds a web Page: What is it?	an organism you think is interesting Page: What is it?	an organism that lives in a group Page: What is it?
an organism that lives in the ocean Page: What is it?	an organism with an interesting life cycle Page: What is it?	an organism that is poisonous Page: What is it?
an organism with four legs Page: What is it?	an organism that can have a lot of different colors Page: What is it?	an organism that has fruit Page: What is it?

© 2018 The Regents of the University of California. All rights reserved. Permission granted to photocopy for classroom use.

Name: _____ Date: _____

Getting Ready to Read:
Blue Whales and Buttercups

Directions:
1. Before reading *Blue Whales and Buttercups*, read the sentences below.
2. If you agree with the sentence, write an "A" on the line before the sentence.
3. If you disagree with the sentence, write a "D" on the line before the sentence.
4. After you read the book, see if your ideas have changed. Be ready to explain your thinking.

_____ All organisms are related.

_____ A blue flower and a blue bird are closely related.

_____ Plants have ways to protect themselves.

_____ Only animals are made of cells.

_____ There are not a lot of differences between the many organisms on Earth.

© 2018 The Regents of the University of California. All rights reserved. Permission granted to photocopy for classroom use.

Name: _____ Date: _____

Asking Questions When Reading:
Blue Whales and Buttercups

Directions:

1. As you read the book, record questions you have in Column 1.

2. If you find the answers to your questions as you read, record your answers in Column 2. Be sure to include the page number from the book where you found the information so you can discuss these ideas with the class.

3. In Column 3, record other ways you could investigate your questions.

Question	Information from the book that helps answer my question	Other ways to investigate my question
	Page:	
	Page:	
	Page:	

© 2018 The Regents of the University of California. All rights reserved. Permission granted to photocopy for classroom use.

Name: _____ Date: _____

Multiple Meaning Words:
Blue Whales and Buttercups

Directions:

Some words can mean more than one thing. For each word in the table:

1. Read the sentence from the book *Blue Whales and Buttercups* that uses the word.
2. Read the two meanings the word can have.
3. Decide which meaning the word has in the sentence from the book and circle that meaning in the table.

Word	Sentence from the book	Meaning 1	Meaning 2
match	It would take about 20 big elephants to **match** the weight of just one blue whale.	a short thin piece of wood used to light a fire	to be the same as
bat	The largest species of **bat** is about 10 times bigger than the smallest species of **bat**.	a flying nocturnal animal	a tool used to hit a ball
slide	Animals may walk, run, fly, swim, or **slide**.	something you find on a playground	to move along a smooth surface

© 2018 The Regents of the University of California. All rights reserved. Permission granted to photocopy for classroom use.

Name: _____ Date: _____

Reading Reflection:
Blue Whales and Buttercups

Directions:

1. Return to the measurements of different organisms on pages 6 and 7 of *Blue Whales and Buttercups*.
2. Answer the questions below.

Is there an object in your classroom similar in size to the wingspan of the bat (1.5 meters) (4.92 feet)?

_____

_____

Is there an object in your classroom similar in size to the tree frog (1 centimeter) (0.39 inches)?

_____

_____

Is there an object in your school similar in size to the height of the elephant (3.5 meters) (11.48 feet)?

_____

_____

© 2018 The Regents of the University of California. All rights reserved. Permission granted to photocopy for classroom use.

Name: _____ Date: _____

Daily Written Reflection

Write about one interesting thing you learned from reading *Blue Whales and Buttercups*.

_____

_____

_____

_____

_____

Make a drawing if it helps you explain your thinking. Label your drawing.

© 2018 The Regents of the University of California. All rights reserved. Permission granted to photocopy for classroom use.

Name: _____ Date: _____

Similarities and Differences: Birds

Directions:

1. With your partner, observe the Bird Cards.
2. In the Similarities column of the table, list the traits that you notice to be similar between birds.
3. In the Differences column, list the traits you notice to be different between birds.

Similarities	Differences

© 2018 The Regents of the University of California. All rights reserved. Permission granted to photocopy for classroom use.

Name: _____ Date: _____

Daily Written Reflection

Write about two ways that scientists can observe organisms.

_____

_____

_____

_____

_____

_____

Make a drawing if it helps you explain your thinking. Label your drawing.

Inheritance and Traits—Lesson 1.4 (optional)

© 2018 The Regents of the University of California. All rights reserved. Permission granted to photocopy for classroom use.

Name: _____ Date: _____

Daily Written Reflection

A black bear and a brown bear have more similar traits than a black bear and a koala bear. Why might this be?

_____

_____

_____

_____

_____

Make a drawing if it helps you explain your thinking. Label your drawing.

© 2018 The Regents of the University of California. All rights reserved. Permission granted to photocopy for classroom use.

Name: _____ Date: _____

Similarities and Variations: Elk Mountain Pack

Directions:

1. Record the similarities and the variations you observe as you discuss the data about wolves.

2. Answer the question at the bottom of the page.

Similarities	Variations

What patterns do you notice?

_____

_____

_____

© 2018 The Regents of the University of California. All rights reserved. Permission granted to photocopy for classroom use.

Name: _____ Date: _____

Asking Science Questions

With your partner, record at least three science questions you have about Wolf 44 or the other wolves in the pack.

Question 1: _____

_____

_____

Question 2: _____

_____

_____

Question 3: _____

_____

_____

Question 4: _____

_____

_____

Question 5: _____

_____

_____

© 2018 The Regents of the University of California. All rights reserved. Permission granted to photocopy for classroom use.

Name: _____ Date: _____

Daily Written Reflection

What did you notice about the traits in your class? Was there a lot of variation? How do you know?

_____

_____

_____

_____

_____

_____

Make a drawing if it helps you explain your thinking. Label your drawing.

© 2018 The Regents of the University of California. All rights reserved. Permission granted to photocopy for classroom use.

You can use this page to record notes or create drawings.

© 2018 The Regents of the University of California. All rights reserved. Permission granted to photocopy for classroom use.

Name: _____ Date: _____

Evidence About Trait Variation

Directions:
1. Read about at least one plant and one animal in *Handbook of Traits*.
2. In the boxes below, record the name of a plant or an animal and list some of the traits that have variation.

Organism:

Traits that have variation:

Organism:

Traits that have variation:

Organism:

Traits that have variation:

Organism:

Traits that have variation:

© 2018 The Regents of the University of California. All rights reserved. Permission granted to photocopy for classroom use.

Name: _____ Date: _____

Word Relationships

Directions:
1. Work with your group to create sentences that use at least two of the word cards in each sentence.
2. Create some sentences that explain what you have been learning about traits.
3. Record a few of the sentences you created.
4. With your group, choose one sentence to share with the class.

variation   trait   organism   species

1. _____

_____

_____

2. _____

_____

_____

3. _____

_____

_____

4. _____

_____

_____

© 2018 The Regents of the University of California. All rights reserved. Permission granted to photocopy for classroom use.

Name: _____ Date: _____

Daily Written Reflection

What are some traits in dogs that have variation?

_____

_____

_____

_____

_____

Make a drawing if it helps you explain your thinking. Label your drawing.

Inheritance and Traits—Lesson 1.7 (optional)

© 2018 The Regents of the University of California. All rights reserved. Permission granted to photocopy for classroom use.

Name: _____ Date: _____

You can use this page to record notes or create drawings.

© 2018 The Regents of the University of California. All rights reserved. Permission granted to photocopy for classroom use.

Name: _____ Date: _____

Gathering Information About Wolves

Directions:

1. With your group, use data from the Elk Mountain Pack Data Cards and information from the books to help you answer the questions on the next page.

2. You can use the scientific language below to help you talk about the data from the cards and ideas from the books.

Scientific language to use when gathering data:

- I observed on the data cards that _____.

- I read in *Handbook of Traits* that _____.

- I read in *Blue Whales and Buttercups* that _____.

© 2018 The Regents of the University of California. All rights reserved. Permission granted to photocopy for classroom use.

Name: _____ Date: _____

Gathering Information About Wolves (continued)

Part 1

What variation did you observe in the photographs of the wolves on the data cards?

Part 2

What did you learn about differences in species? Give examples from *Blue Whales and Buttercups* and *Handbook of Traits*.

Part 3

What science words will you use to share your ideas about differences in wolves?

© 2018 The Regents of the University of California. All rights reserved. Permission granted to photocopy for classroom use.

Name: _____ Date: _____

Reflecting on Why Wolves Are Different

Directions:

1. Read the question below.
2. Based on the information you gathered with your group, write your ideas about the answer to the question.

Question: Why are wolves different even though they are all the same species?

_____

_____

_____

_____

© 2018 The Regents of the University of California. All rights reserved. Permission granted to photocopy for classroom use.

Name: _____ Date: _____

Chapter 1: Check Your Understanding

This is a chance for you to reflect on your learning so far. This is not a test. Be open and truthful when you respond.

Scientists investigate in order to figure out how things work. Am I getting closer to figuring out why Wolf 44 has the traits it has?

I understand why Wolf 44's trait for fur color is similar to the fur color of wolves in the Bison Valley Pack.　_____ Yes　_____ Not yet

I understand why Wolf 44 has some traits that are similar to the wolves in the Elk Mountain Pack.　_____ Yes　_____ Not yet

I understand why Wolf 44 can have traits that are different from other wolves in Graystone National Park.　_____ Yes　_____ Not yet

I understand that scientists answer their questions by looking for patterns in data.　_____ Yes　_____ Not yet

I understand that the methods scientists use to investigate are determined by the questions they ask.　_____ Yes　_____ Not yet

What are you still wondering about the traits of Wolf 44?

_____

_____

_____

© 2018 The Regents of the University of California. All rights reserved. Permission granted to photocopy for classroom use.

Name: _____ Date: _____

Daily Written Reflection

Explain why roses can be so many different colors even though they are all roses.

_____

_____

_____

_____

_____

_____

Make a drawing if it helps you explain your thinking. Label your drawing.

© 2018 The Regents of the University of California. All rights reserved. Permission granted to photocopy for classroom use.

You can use this page to record notes or create drawings.

© 2018 The Regents of the University of California. All rights reserved. Permission granted to photocopy for classroom use.

Name: _____ Date: _____

Similarities and Variations: Bison Valley Pack

Directions:

1. Record the similarities and the variations you observe as you discuss the data.
2. Record the traits that have similarity and the traits that have variation.
3. Answer the question on the next page.

Similarities	Traits that have similarity

Variations	Traits that have variation

© 2018 The Regents of the University of California. All rights reserved. Permission granted to photocopy for classroom use.

Name: _____ Date: _____

Similarities and Variations: Bison Valley Pack (continued)

What patterns do you notice within the Bison Valley Pack?

_____

_____

_____

_____

© 2018 The Regents of the University of California. All rights reserved. Permission granted to photocopy for classroom use.

Name: _____ Date: _____

Similarities and Variations:
Elk Mountain Pack and Bison Valley Pack

Directions:

1. Record the similarities and the variations you observe between the two wolf packs as you discuss the data.
2. Record the traits that have similarity and the traits that have variation.
3. Answer the question on the next page.

Similarities	Traits that have similarity

Variations	Traits that have variation

© 2018 The Regents of the University of California. All rights reserved. Permission granted to photocopy for classroom use.

Name: _____ Date: _____

Similarities and Variations:
Elk Mountain Pack and Bison Valley Pack (continued)

What patterns do you notice between the two wolf packs?

_____

_____

_____

_____

_____

© 2018 The Regents of the University of California. All rights reserved. Permission granted to photocopy for classroom use.

Name: _____ Date: _____

Daily Written Reflection

What is one thing you found interesting about fruit fly families?

_____

_____

_____

_____

_____

Make a drawing if it helps you explain your thinking. Label your drawing.

© 2018 The Regents of the University of California. All rights reserved. Permission granted to photocopy for classroom use.

You can use this page to record notes or create drawings.

© 2018 The Regents of the University of California. All rights reserved. Permission granted to photocopy for classroom use.

Name: _____ Date: _____

Patterns in Parents and Offspring

Directions:
1. In *Handbook of Traits,* read about each of the organisms listed.
2. For each organism, record a trait the organism has.
3. Record the trait that each parent has.
4. Record the trait that the offspring has.
5. Answer the question on the next page.

Organism: Harlequin Poison Frog

Trait: _____

Parent 1: _____

Parent 2: _____

Offspring: _____

Organism: Snapdragon Plant

Trait: _____

Parent 1: _____

Parent 2: _____

Offspring: _____

Organism: House Cat

Trait: _____

Parent 1: _____

Parent 2: _____

Offspring: _____

© 2018 The Regents of the University of California. All rights reserved. Permission granted to photocopy for classroom use.

Patterns in Parents and Offspring (continued)

Organism: Mexican Tetra

Trait: _____

Parent 1: _____

Parent 2: _____

Offspring: _____

Organism: Domestic Dog

Trait: _____

Parent 1: _____

Parent 2: _____

Offspring: _____

What new ideas do you have about offspring and parents after reading *Handbook of Traits*?

_____

_____

_____

© 2018 The Regents of the University of California. All rights reserved. Permission granted to photocopy for classroom use.

Name: _____ Date: _____

Modeling Patterns in Parents and Offspring

Use the Parent and Offspring Traits Model to answer the questions below.

Record a trait you chose for one of the deer offspring.

_____

How does this trait compare to the traits of the parents?

_____

_____

Record a trait you chose for a different deer offspring.

_____

How does this trait compare to the traits of the parents?

_____

_____

What pattern did you notice about the traits of offspring and parent deer?

_____

_____

_____

© 2018 The Regents of the University of California. All rights reserved. Permission granted to photocopy for classroom use.

Name: _____ Date: _____

Daily Written Reflection

Look at pages 32–33 in your notebook. Describe a pattern of traits between parents and offspring that you read about organisms in *Handbook of Traits*.

_____

_____

_____

_____

_____

_____

Make a drawing if it helps you explain your thinking. Label your drawing.

© 2018 The Regents of the University of California. All rights reserved. Permission granted to photocopy for classroom use.

Name: _____ Date: _____

Getting Ready to Read: *The Code*

Directions:
1. Before reading *The Code*, read the sentences below.
2. If you agree with the sentence, write an "A" on the line before the sentence.
3. If you disagree with the sentence, write a "D" on the line before the sentence.
4. After you read the book, see if your ideas have changed. Be ready to explain your thinking.

_____ Genes tell your body what color to make your eyes and hair.

_____ All humans have some of the same genes.

_____ Babies look exactly the same as their parents.

_____ Humans have many of the same traits because they have many of the same genes.

_____ Only humans have genes.

© 2018 The Regents of the University of California. All rights reserved. Permission granted to photocopy for classroom use.

Name: _____ Date: _____

Asking Questions When Reading: *The Code*

Directions:

1. As you read the book, record questions you have in Column 1.
2. If you find the answers to your questions as you read, record your answers in Column 2. Be sure to include the page number from the book where you found the information so you can discuss these ideas with the class.
3. In Column 3, record other ways you could investigate your questions.

Question	Information from the book that helps answer my question	Other ways to investigate my question
	Page:	
	Page:	
	Page:	

© 2018 The Regents of the University of California. All rights reserved. Permission granted to photocopy for classroom use.

Name: _____ Date: _____

Multiple Meaning Words: *The Code*

Directions:

Some words can mean more than one thing. For each word in the table:

1. Read the sentence from the book *The Code* that uses the word.
2. Read the two meanings the word can have.
3. Decide which meaning the word has in the sentence from the book and circle that meaning in the table.

Word	Sentence from the book	Meaning 1	Meaning 2
face	How are these **faces** similar?	to position yourself with your body toward something	the front part of a person's head
live	Some of us **live** with our birth parents.	not dead	to stay in a place
passed	Even if we never meet our birth parents, they have **passed** traits down to us.	gave something from one person to another	decided not to do something

© 2018 The Regents of the University of California. All rights reserved. Permission granted to photocopy for classroom use.

Reading Reflection: *The Code*

Turn to page 7 in *The Code* and read the text again. The text says that traits such as hair color, eye color, having eyes, having a mouth, and having a nose can be inherited traits. What are some other traits that you think are inherited?

_____

_____

_____

_____

© 2018 The Regents of the University of California. All rights reserved. Permission granted to photocopy for classroom use.

Name: _____ Date: _____

Daily Written Reflection

Based on what you read in *The Code*, what ideas do you have about what genes do?

_____

_____

_____

_____

_____

Make a drawing if it helps you explain your thinking. Label your drawing.

© 2018 The Regents of the University of California. All rights reserved. Permission granted to photocopy for classroom use.

Name: _____ Date: _____

Making a Creature Offspring

Directions:

1. Using your Parent 1 and Parent 2 instruction strips, find the matches in Column 1.
2. When you find a match, look in Column 2 to see the part of your creature that you will make.
3. In Column 3, make a check mark next to each trait that your creature has.

Instructions	What to build	Creature has this trait
& &	a green body and head	
& =	a yellow body and head	
¶ ¶	four legs	
X X	a long red tail	
X <	a short red tail	
@ @	a round head	
% %	a red mouth	
◊ ◊	short red horns	
◊ //	long red horns	
+ +	green eyes	
+ #	red eyes	
O O	short red nose	
O ⇨	long red nose	

© 2018 The Regents of the University of California. All rights reserved. Permission granted to photocopy for classroom use.

Name: _____ Date: _____

Similarities and Variations: Creature Offspring

Directions:
1. Observe three offspring.
2. In Column 1, record the traits that have similarity.
3. In Column 2, record the traits that have variations.
4. Answer the questions on the next page.

Similarities	Variations

© 2018 The Regents of the University of California. All rights reserved. Permission granted to photocopy for classroom use.

Similarities and Variations: Creature Offspring (continued)

How did the offspring get traits that are similar?

_____

_____

_____

How did the offspring get traits that are different?

_____

_____

_____

What could have caused some traits to be similar and some to be different?

_____

_____

_____

_____

_____

© 2018 The Regents of the University of California. All rights reserved. Permission granted to photocopy for classroom use.

Name: _____ Date: _____

Daily Written Reflection

Explain how the creature you made out of clay got its traits.

_____

_____

_____

_____

_____

Make a drawing if it helps you explain your thinking. Label your drawing.

© 2018 The Regents of the University of California. All rights reserved. Permission granted to photocopy for classroom use.

Name: _____ Date: _____

Modeling Trait Inheritance

Directions:
1. Select one offspring from your digital model.
2. Draw your offspring and label its traits.
3. Answer the questions below to explain how the offspring got its traits.

What patterns did you notice between the traits you labeled in the offspring and the traits in the parents?

_____

_____

_____

Why did different offspring have different traits from one another, even though they all had the same parents?

_____

_____

_____

© 2018 The Regents of the University of California. All rights reserved. Permission granted to photocopy for classroom use.

Name: _____ Date: _____

Word Relationships

Directions:
1. Work with your group to create sentences that use at least two of the word cards in each sentence.
2. Create some sentences that explain what you have been learning about traits.
3. Record a few of the sentences you created.
4. With your group, choose one sentence to share with the class.

trait   variation   inherit   reproduce   offspring   genes

1. _____

_____

_____

2. _____

_____

_____

3. _____

_____

_____

4. _____

_____

_____

© 2018 The Regents of the University of California. All rights reserved. Permission granted to photocopy for classroom use.

Name: _____ Date: _____

Wolf 44's Fur Color

Directions:

1. Record the trait you will be observing.
2. Record the parents and the offspring.
3. Review the data and then record the traits for Parent 1, Parent 2, and the offspring.

Trait: _____

Parent 1: _____

- Trait: _____

Parent 2: _____

- Trait: _____

Offspring: _____

- Trait: _____

© 2018 The Regents of the University of California. All rights reserved. Permission granted to photocopy for classroom use.

Name: _____ Date: _____

Daily Written Reflection

Why don't siblings with the same birth parents always have similar traits to one another?

_____

_____

_____

_____

_____

_____

Make a drawing if it helps you explain your thinking. Label your drawing.

© 2018 The Regents of the University of California. All rights reserved. Permission granted to photocopy for classroom use.

Name: _____ Date: _____

You can use this page to record notes or create drawings.

© 2018 The Regents of the University of California. All rights reserved. Permission granted to photocopy for classroom use.

Name: _____ Date: _____

Gathering Data About Traits

Directions:

1. With your group, use data from the Wolf Family Data Cards and information from the books to help you answer the questions on the next page.

2. You can use the scientific language below to help you talk about the data from the cards and ideas from the books.

Scientific language to use when gathering data:

- I observed on the data cards that _____.

- I read in *The Code* that _____.

- I read in *Handbook of Traits* that _____.

© 2018 The Regents of the University of California. All rights reserved. Permission granted to photocopy for classroom use.

Gathering Data About Traits (continued)

Part 1

What variation in fur color did you observe in the wolf family trees?

Part 2

What did you learn about where traits come from? Give examples from *The Code* and *Handbook of Traits*.

Part 3

What science words will you use when writing about Wolf 44?

© 2018 The Regents of the University of California. All rights reserved. Permission granted to photocopy for classroom use.

Name: _____ Date: _____

Scientific Explanation of Wolf 44's Fur Color

Directions:
1. Write a scientific explanation that answers the question below.
2. Your audience is the students of Graystone Elementary School.

Question: Why is Wolf 44's color similar to one pack but different from the other?

_____

_____

_____

_____

_____

_____

_____

_____

_____

_____

_____

© 2018 The Regents of the University of California. All rights reserved. Permission granted to photocopy for classroom use.

Name: _____ Date: _____

Chapter 2: Check Your Understanding

This is a chance for you to reflect on your learning so far. This is not a test. Be open and truthful when you respond.

Scientists investigate in order to figure out how things work. Am I getting closer to figuring out why Wolf 44 has the traits it has?

I understand why Wolf 44's trait for fur color is similar to the fur color of wolves in the Bison Valley Pack. ____ Yes ____ Not yet

I understand why Wolf 44 has some traits that are similar to the wolves in the Elk Mountain Pack. ____ Yes ____ Not yet

I understand why Wolf 44 can have traits that are different from other wolves in Graystone National Park. ____ Yes ____ Not yet

I understand that scientists answer their questions by looking for patterns in data. ____ Yes ____ Not yet

I understand that the methods scientists use to investigate are determined by the questions they ask. ____ Yes ____ Not yet

What are you still wondering about the traits of Wolf 44?

_____

_____

_____

© 2018 The Regents of the University of California. All rights reserved. Permission granted to photocopy for classroom use.

Name: _____ Date: _____

Daily Written Reflection

Can traits come from somewhere besides birth parents? Explain your thinking.

_____

_____

_____

_____

_____

_____

Make a drawing if it helps you explain your thinking. Label your drawing.

© 2018 The Regents of the University of California. All rights reserved. Permission granted to photocopy for classroom use.

Name: _____ Date: _____

Investigating Data About Flamingos

Directions:
1. Record the questions you had when you observed the flamingo data.
2. Record the question you are going to investigate as you return to the data about flamingos.
3. Record the new ideas you have or patterns you notice.

Questions I have about the data:

_____

_____

_____

_____

_____

Question to investigate:

_____

_____

New ideas or patterns from the data:

_____

_____

_____

_____

© 2018 The Regents of the University of California. All rights reserved. Permission granted to photocopy for classroom use.

Name: _____ Date: _____

Daily Written Reflection

Describe a pattern you noticed in the Flamingo Family Data Cards.

_____

_____

_____

_____

_____

_____

Make a drawing if it helps you explain your thinking. Label your drawing.

Inheritance and Traits—Lesson 3.2 (optional)

© 2018 The Regents of the University of California. All rights reserved. Permission granted to photocopy for classroom use.

Name: _____ Date: _____

Getting Ready to Read:
How the Sparrow Learned Its Song

Directions:

1. Before reading *How the Sparrow Learned Its Song*, read the sentences below.
2. If you agree with the sentence, write an "A" on the line before the sentence.
3. If you disagree with the sentence, write a "D" on the line before the sentence.
4. After you read the book, see if your ideas have changed. Be ready to explain your thinking.

_____ Organisms can learn new traits.

_____ The environment cannot change an organism's traits.

_____ All traits are passed down to offspring.

_____ Bears inherit the trait of hunting from their parents.

_____ Some traits result from both inheritance and interaction with the environment.

© 2018 The Regents of the University of California. All rights reserved. Permission granted to photocopy for classroom use.

Name: _____ Date: _____

Asking Questions When Reading:
How the Sparrow Learned Its Song

Directions:

1. As you read the book, record questions you have in Column 1.
2. If you find the answers to your questions as you read, record your answers in Column 2. Be sure to include the page number from the book where you found the information so you can discuss these ideas with the class.
3. In Column 3, record other ways you could investigate your questions.

Question	Information from the book that helps answer my question	Other ways to investigate my question
	Page:	
	Page:	
	Page:	

© 2018 The Regents of the University of California. All rights reserved. Permission granted to photocopy for classroom use.

Name: _____ Date: _____

Multiple Meaning Words:
How the Sparrow Learned Its Song

Directions:

Some words can mean more than one thing. For each word in the table:

1. Read the sentence from the book *How the Sparrow Learned Its Song* that uses the word.
2. Read the two meanings the word can have.
3. Decide which meaning the word has in the sentence from the book and circle that meaning in the table.

Word	Sentence from the book	Meaning 1	Meaning 2
play	For example, you may **play** sports and build up your muscles.	to take part in a sport or game	a show with actors on a stage
pass	The spikey crab can't **pass** on its spikes to its offspring.	to leave behind, usually in a race	to move from one person to another
right	The monkey's offspring will have to learn how to make the **right** alarm call.	the opposite of left	correct
note	It is singing a song with many different **notes**.	a short written message	a sound made by an instrument

© 2018 The Regents of the University of California. All rights reserved. Permission granted to photocopy for classroom use.

Name: _____ Date: _____

Reading Reflection:
How the Sparrow Learned Its Song

How did the sparrow learn to sing its song?

_____

_____

_____

Why could a bear never learn to sing like a sparrow?

_____

_____

_____

© 2018 The Regents of the University of California. All rights reserved. Permission granted to photocopy for classroom use.

Name: _____ Date: _____

Daily Written Reflection

Name five traits that you got from your environment.

_____

_____

_____

_____

_____

Make a drawing if it helps you explain your thinking. Label your drawing.

© 2018 The Regents of the University of California. All rights reserved. Permission granted to photocopy for classroom use.

Name: _____ Date: _____

Scientific Explanation of Wolf 44's Hunting Style

Directions:

1. Write a scientific explanation that answers the question below.
2. Your audience is the students of Graystone Elementary School.

Question: Why isn't Wolf 44 like the Bison Valley Pack in hunting style?

Wolf 44 isn't like the Bison Valley Pack in hunting style because _____

_____

_____

_____

_____

_____

_____

_____

_____

_____

_____

© 2018 The Regents of the University of California. All rights reserved. Permission granted to photocopy for classroom use.

Name: _____ Date: _____

Investigating Celery

Directions:

1. With your group, set up your celery investigation.
2. Observe the celery and the water.
3. Record your observations.
4. In the box, you can draw what you observe, if it helps you explain your thinking.

Observations:

_____

_____

_____

_____

Make a drawing if it helps you explain your thinking. Label your drawing.

© 2018 The Regents of the University of California. All rights reserved. Permission granted to photocopy for classroom use.

Name: _____ Date: _____

Daily Written Reflection

What other traits do you think Wolf 44 could get from its environment?

_____

_____

_____

_____

_____

Make a drawing if it helps you explain your thinking. Label your drawing.

© 2018 The Regents of the University of California. All rights reserved. Permission granted to photocopy for classroom use.

Name: _____ Date: _____

Completing the Celery Investigation

Directions:

1. With your group, observe what happened to the celery in each of the cups.
2. Record your observations in the table. Don't forget to record the color of the water in each cup.
3. Discuss the questions on the bottom of the page and record your answers.

Cup 1 water color:	Cup 2 water color:	Cup 3 water color:

How did the celery get the trait of being blue-green?

_____

_____

Can the environment affect inherited traits? Explain your thinking.

_____

_____

_____

© 2018 The Regents of the University of California. All rights reserved. Permission granted to photocopy for classroom use.

Name: _____ Date: _____

Reading About Traits

Directions:

1. In *Handbook of Traits,* locate the organisms listed in Column 1. You can also choose your own organism to research.
2. Decide whether any of the traits listed for the organism result from both inheritance and the environment. Record those traits in Column 2.
3. Use information from the text to explain how the organism got its trait. Record that information in Column 3.

Organism	Trait that results from both inheritance and the environment	Explain how the organism got its trait.
Peppered Moth	Page:	
Snowy Owl	Page:	
White Willow Tree	Page:	
	Page:	

© 2018 The Regents of the University of California. All rights reserved. Permission granted to photocopy for classroom use.

Name: _____ Date: _____

Daily Written Reflection

Write about one organism you read about in *Handbook of Traits* that had an interesting trait. How did the organism get that trait?

_____

_____

_____

_____

_____

Make a drawing if it helps you explain your thinking. Label your drawing.

© 2018 The Regents of the University of California. All rights reserved. Permission granted to photocopy for classroom use.

Name: _____ Date: _____

Modeling How the Environment Affects Traits

Directions:
1. Complete the digital Environment and Inheritance Model.
2. Answer the questions on this and the next page.

In Family 1, what environment did you choose for the offspring?

_____

Why did you choose that environment?

_____

_____

_____

Describe the traits of the offspring you chose for Family 2.

_____

_____

Why did you choose those traits for the offspring?

_____

_____

_____

_____

© 2018 The Regents of the University of California. All rights reserved. Permission granted to photocopy for classroom use.

Modeling How the Environment Affects Traits (continued)

In Family 3, what traits for size and color did you choose for the parents?

_____

_____

Why did you choose those traits for the parents?

_____

_____

_____

© 2018 The Regents of the University of California. All rights reserved. Permission granted to photocopy for classroom use.

Data About Wolf Size

Bison Valley Pack

Wolf number	Weight
Wolf 60 (male)	46 kg (102 lbs.)
Wolf 61 (female)	39 kg (87 lbs.)
Wolf 62 (male)	44 kg (97 lbs.)
Wolf 63 (female)	36 kg (80 lbs.)
Wolf 64 (female)	—
Wolf 65 (male)	43 kg (95 lbs.)
Wolf 66 (female)	42 kg (93 lbs.)
Wolf 67 (male)	45 kg (100 lbs.)
Wolf 68 (female)	41 kg (91 lbs.)

Elk Mountain Pack

Wolf number	Weight
Wolf 40 (female)	53 kg (116 lbs.)
Wolf 41 (female)	51 kg (113 lbs.)
Wolf 42 (male)	—
Wolf 43 (male)	57 kg (127 lbs.)
Wolf 44 (male)	49 kg (108 lbs)
Wolf 45 (male)	55 kg (122 lbs.)
Wolf 46 (female)	49 kg (108 lbs.)
Wolf 47 (female)	50 kg (110 lbs.)
Wolf 48 (male)	59 kg (130 lbs.)

© 2018 The Regents of the University of California. All rights reserved. Permission granted to photocopy for classroom use.

Data About Wolf Size (continued)

Wolf Weights in Both Packs

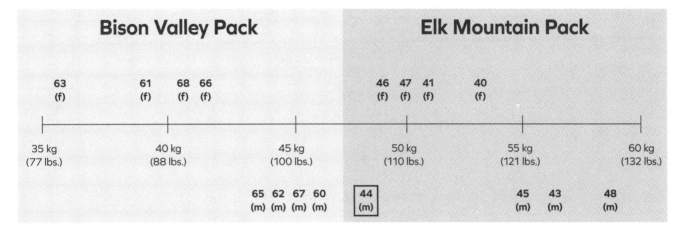

Kilograms of Food Eaten Per Day

Elk Mountain Pack	4 kg (8 lbs.) of food per day
Bison Valley Pack	2 kg (5 lbs.) of food per day
Wolf 44	4 kg (8 lbs.) pounds of food per day

© 2018 The Regents of the University of California. All rights reserved. Permission granted to photocopy for classroom use.

Discussing Data About Traits

Directions:

1. With your group, use data from the Wolf Family Data Cards, data from pages 70–71 in your notebook, and information from the books to help you answer the questions on the next page.

2. You can use the scientific language below to help you talk about the data about wolves and ideas from the books.

Scientific language to use when discussing data:

- The data shows that _____.

- This means that _____.

- I read in *How the Sparrow Learned Its Song* that _____.

- I read in *Handbook of Traits* that _____.

© 2018 The Regents of the University of California. All rights reserved. Permission granted to photocopy for classroom use.

Name: _____ Date: _____

Discussing Data About Traits (continued)

Part 1

What did you learn about Wolf 44's size from the Wolf Family Data Cards and the data on pages 70–71 in your notebook?

Part 2

What new information did you learn about where traits come from? Give examples from *How the Sparrow Learned Its Song* and *Handbook of Traits*.

Part 3

What science words will you use when writing about where traits can come from?

Part 4

Based on the information you gathered, why isn't Wolf 44 more like the Bison Valley pack in size?

© 2018 The Regents of the University of California. All rights reserved. Permission granted to photocopy for classroom use.

Name: _____ Date: _____

Daily Written Reflection

What questions do you still have about Wolf 44?

_____

_____

_____

_____

_____

_____

Make a drawing if it helps you explain your thinking. Label your drawing.

© 2018 The Regents of the University of California. All rights reserved. Permission granted to photocopy for classroom use.

Name: _____ Date: _____

Word Relationships

Directions:

1. Work with your group to create sentences that use at least two of the word cards in each sentence.

2. Create some sentences that explain what you have been learning about traits.

3. Record a few of the sentences you created.

4. With your group, choose one sentence to share with the class.

inherit   trait   organism   environment

1. _____

_____

_____

2. _____

_____

_____

3. _____

_____

_____

4. _____

_____

_____

© 2018 The Regents of the University of California. All rights reserved. Permission granted to photocopy for classroom use.

Name: _____ Date: _____

Chapter 3: Check Your Understanding

This is a chance for you to reflect on your learning so far. This is not a test. Be open and truthful when you respond.

Scientists investigate in order to figure out how things work. Am I getting closer to figuring out why Wolf 44 has the traits it has?

I understand why Wolf 44's trait for fur color is similar to the fur color of wolves in the Bison Valley Pack.   ____ Yes   ____ Not yet

I understand why Wolf 44 has some traits that are similar to the wolves in the Elk Mountain Pack.   ____ Yes   ____ Not yet

I understand why Wolf 44 can have traits that are different from other wolves in Graystone National Park.   ____ Yes   ____ Not yet

I understand that scientists answer their questions by looking for patterns in data.   ____ Yes   ____ Not yet

I understand that the methods scientists use to investigate are determined by the questions they ask.   ____ Yes   ____ Not yet

What are you still wondering about the traits of Wolf 44?

_____

_____

_____

© 2018 The Regents of the University of California. All rights reserved. Permission granted to photocopy for classroom use.

Name: _____ Date: _____

Daily Written Reflection

Scientists ask questions they can investigate. What are some ways you have investigated your questions in this unit?

_____

_____

_____

_____

_____

_____

Make a drawing if it helps you explain your thinking. Label your drawing.

© 2018 The Regents of the University of California. All rights reserved. Permission granted to photocopy for classroom use.

Name: _____ Date: _____

Getting Ready to Read: *Scorpion Scientist*

Directions:
1. Before reading *Scorpion Scientist*, read the sentences below.
2. If you agree with the sentence, write an "A" on the line before the sentence.
3. If you disagree with the sentence, write a "D" on the line before the sentence.
4. After you read the book, see if your ideas have changed. Be ready to explain your thinking.

_____ All scorpions are in the same species.

_____ Scorpions lay eggs like spiders do.

_____ Scientists use their own observations, as well as observations other scientists have made, to answer their questions.

_____ Scientists can tell just by looking at DNA if organisms are the same species.

_____ Scientists keep their discoveries secret.

© 2018 The Regents of the University of California. All rights reserved. Permission granted to photocopy for classroom use.

Name: _____ Date: _____

You can use this page to record notes or create drawings.

© 2018 The Regents of the University of California. All rights reserved. Permission granted to photocopy for classroom use.

Name: _____ Date: _____

How Scientists Investigate Questions:
Scorpion Scientist

Directions:

1. Read each question in Column 1 and think about how Esposito investigates each question.

2. In Column 2, record the different ways Esposito investigates her questions.

3. Answer the question on the next page.

Esposito's question	How does Esposito investigate her question?
Are the Valley Scorpions a new species? (page 15)	
Are the genes that the Valley Scorpions inherited different from other scorpions' genes? (page 16)	
Do the Valley Scorpions live in a different environment from other scorpions? (page 17)	
Do the Valley Scorpions have different traits from other scorpions? (page 18)	

© 2018 The Regents of the University of California. All rights reserved. Permission granted to photocopy for classroom use.

Name: _____ Date: _____

How Scientists Investigate Questions:
Scorpion Scientist (continued)

What patterns did Esposito notice about Valley Scorpions compared with other scorpions? To help you think about patterns, think about the observations Esposito made about the genes, environment, and traits of Valley Scorpions.

_____

_____

_____

_____

© 2018 The Regents of the University of California. All rights reserved. Permission granted to photocopy for classroom use.

Multiple Meaning Words: *Scorpion Scientist*

Directions:

Some words can mean more than one thing. For each word in the table:

1. Read the sentence from the book *How the Sparrow Learned Its Song* that uses the word.
2. Read the two meanings the word can have.
3. Decide which meaning the word has in the sentence from the book and circle that meaning in the table.

Word	Sentence from the book	Meaning 1	Meaning 2
call	Scientists **call** these big and small differences variation.	to give a name to something	use the phone to talk to someone
recorded	She also uses observations that other scientists have **recorded**.	wrote down information	saved sounds or music to listen to later
light	Scorpions glow when you shine a special **light** on them.	to not weigh much	a tool that makes things easy to see

© 2018 The Regents of the University of California. All rights reserved. Permission granted to photocopy for classroom use.

Name: _____ Date: _____

Reading Reflection: *Scorpion Scientist*

Directions:

After a lot of investigating, Esposito used the answers to all her smaller questions to make a claim. A claim is an answer to a question.

1. What is Esposito's claim?
2. Do you agree or disagree with her claim? Circle one answer below.
3. Explain why you agree or disagree with Esposito's claim.

Claim:

_____

_____

I agree / disagree with Esposito's claim because _____

_____

_____

_____

_____

© 2018 The Regents of the University of California. All rights reserved. Permission granted to photocopy for classroom use.

Daily Written Reflection

Think about one question that the scientist in *Scorpion Scientist* asked. How did she investigate that question? What did she find out?

_____

_____

_____

_____

_____

Make a drawing if it helps you explain your thinking. Label your drawing.

© 2018 The Regents of the University of California. All rights reserved. Permission granted to photocopy for classroom use.

Name: _____ Date: _____

Asking Questions About Sparrows

Directions:

1. Choose three questions about the traits of the sparrows that you want to investigate.
2. Record your questions in the first column.
3. In the second column, record what you will look for on the Sparrow Family Data Cards to help you answer each question.

Question about sparrow traits	What I would look for in the data to answer my question

© 2018 The Regents of the University of California. All rights reserved. Permission granted to photocopy for classroom use.

Name: _____ Date: _____

Daily Written Reflection

What is one question you still have about sparrows? How might you investigate this question?

_____

_____

_____

_____

_____

Make a drawing if it helps you explain your thinking. Label your drawing.

Inheritance and Traits—Lesson 4.3 (optional)

© 2018 The Regents of the University of California. All rights reserved. Permission granted to photocopy for classroom use.

Name: _____ Date: _____

Recording Ideas About Sparrows

Directions:

1. Record each of the traits you think the Family 1 offspring could have, based on the data about sparrows.

2. Answer the questions to explain how the offspring would get its traits.

Trait: thickness of stripes on head

Possible trait for the offspring: _____

Does the offspring inherit this trait? How do you know?

_____

_____

_____

Does this trait result from the environment? How do you know?

_____

_____

_____

© 2018 The Regents of the University of California. All rights reserved. Permission granted to photocopy for classroom use.

Name: _____ Date: _____

Recording Ideas About Sparrows (continued)

Trait: beak color

Possible trait for the offspring: _____

Does the offspring inherit this trait? How do you know?

_____

_____

_____

Does this trait result from the environment? How do you know?

_____

_____

_____

© 2018 The Regents of the University of California. All rights reserved. Permission granted to photocopy for classroom use.

Name: _____ Date: _____

Recording Ideas About Sparrows (continued)

Trait: song type

Possible trait for the offspring: _____

Does the offspring inherit this trait? How do you know?

_____

_____

_____

Does this trait result from the environment? How do you know?

_____

_____

_____

© 2018 The Regents of the University of California. All rights reserved. Permission granted to photocopy for classroom use.

Name: _____ Date: _____

Recording Ideas About Sparrows (continued)

Trait: body size

Possible trait for the offspring: _____

Does the offspring inherit this trait? How do you know?

_____

_____

_____

Does this trait result from the environment? How do you know?

_____

_____

_____

© 2018 The Regents of the University of California. All rights reserved. Permission granted to photocopy for classroom use.

Drawing the Sparrow Offspring

Directions:

1. Using the possible traits you recorded on pages 87–90, draw the sparrow offspring for Sparrow Family 1.

2. Include labels in your drawing.

© 2018 The Regents of the University of California. All rights reserved. Permission granted to photocopy for classroom use.

Chapter 4: Check Your Understanding

This is a chance for you to reflect on your learning so far. This is not a test. Be open and truthful when you respond.

Scientists investigate in order to figure out how things work. Am I getting closer to figuring out why organisms have the traits they have?

I understand why an organism can have traits that are similar to other organisms in its family. _____ Yes _____ Not yet

I understand why an organism can have traits that are similar to other organisms of the same species that are not in its family. _____ Yes _____ Not yet

I understand why an organism can have traits that are different from other organisms of the same species. _____ Yes _____ Not yet

I understand that scientists answer their questions by looking for patterns in data. _____ Yes _____ Not yet

I understand that the methods scientists use to investigate are determined by the questions they ask. _____ Yes _____ Not yet

What are you still wondering about the traits of organisms?

_____

_____

_____

© 2018 The Regents of the University of California. All rights reserved. Permission granted to photocopy for classroom use.

Glossary

data: observations or measurements recorded in an investigation
datos: observaciones o mediciones apuntadas en una investigación

environment: all the living and nonliving things in an area
ambiente: todo (viviente y no viviente) lo que hay en un área

explanation: a description of how something works or why something happens
explicación: una descripción de cómo algo funciona o por qué algo pasa

genes: instructions for making a living thing that are in cells and passed from parents to offspring
genes: instrucciones para desarrollar un ser viviente que están en las células y pasan de padres a descendencia

inherit: to get something that is passed down
heredar: recibir algo que es transmitido de antes

investigate: to try to learn more about something
investigar: intentar aprender más acerca de algo

observe: to use any of the five senses to gather information about something
observar: usar cualquiera de los cinco sentidos para recolectar información acerca de algo

offspring: living things that come from parents
descendencia: seres vivientes que provienen de padres

organism: a living thing, such as a plant or an animal
organismo: un ser viviente, por ejemplo una planta o un animal

© 2018 The Regents of the University of California. All rights reserved. Permission granted to photocopy for classroom use.

Glossary (continued)

pattern: something we observe to be similar over and over again
patrón: algo que observamos que sea similar una y otra vez

reproduce: to make offspring
reproducir: generar descendencia

species: a group of organisms that are closely related to each other
especie: un grupo de organismos que están cercanamente emparentados entre sí

trait: something that can be observed about an organism, such as color or size
rasgo: algo que se puede observar acerca de un organismo, como el color o el tamaño

variation: differences
variación: diferencias

© 2018 The Regents of the University of California. All rights reserved. Permission granted to photocopy for classroom use.